# YOU GOT THAT

# FROM ME

*Understanding the Truth About God's Love*

## 10 Lesson Bible Study

## Trecia Willcutt

*You Got That From Me*

First edition. April 27, 2022.

Written by Trecia Willcutt.

# Table of Contents

# Lesson 1

## God *is* Love

On August 13, 2017, Sunday afternoon, while I was praying the Lord spoke to my heart and said, "Go tell people how good I am." That night, at the church where we were pastors at the time, I shared with our congregation about the goodness of our heavenly Father. From that night on I have continually taught, exhorted, preached, spoke, and ministered about the goodness of God. However; the truth is, I myself did not even know of the depth or the scope of the Father's love. I talked about the goodness of God, the goodness of his Son, the goodness of the Holy Spirit, and even the goodness of the Word but I did not fully comprehend the truth of the love of God. But oh how that has changed over the course of the last few years!

Let me begin by explaining some of the completely wrong ideas I had about our gracious, loving, wonderful Father. For some reason, I thought that God was always waiting to punish me for something I did wrong. If I made a mistake, if I said something I should not have said that hurt someone's feelings, if I started talking negatively about someone, if I shorted my tithes by two dollars, if I did not fast enough that week, if I fell asleep before reading my Bible for an hour, I thought God would punish me by not answering any of my prayers. I thought that when I did something, anything, wrong God would withhold goodness from me. I believed that if I gave into temptation then God would withdraw himself from me; like literally ignore me, until I proved myself worthy enough to gain his trust again. Then, he would fellowship with me and I could "feel" his Spirit and goodness while I was praying or worshipping him. I know that all sounds ridiculous and I am probably the only person on the face of the earth that has ever thought that is how God feels about us or that is how God treats us when we do wrong.

But then I had an encounter with the love of Jesus like I had never had before and it began to radically change my wrong ideas about God. I went from thinking God is continually waiting to punish his children to understanding the truth about the passionate, longsuffering, endless and enduring love the Father has for his children. So let's begin this journey of love by establishing the true nature of God. I want to encourage you to read closely, open your heart, and have ears to hear the truth. Many times I have heard this statement, "God is good…all the time" but then I hear from the same people, "So and so was just diagnosed with cancer, you think

2

God is trying to get their attention?" Or, "Did you hear about that terrible accident that killed that mom and her 3 children? Well, God has a plan", implying God himself caused that accident because everything that happens good or bad is part of God's sovereign plan for people's lives. If you have ever said or ever believed either one of those statements to be true of God, you DO NOT know the nature of God himself. Now stay with me because I, at one time, believed that is how God operated in people's lives also. I thought everything bad that happened was a part of God's divine plan for my life because I simply did not know the Word of God.

Let's start with James 1:17:

_____

_____

_____

_____

Is cancer good or perfect? Is a tragic car accident good or perfect? Then it did NOT come from God. God does not strike people down with cancer or any other sickness or disease. God does not orchestrate tragedy, heartbreak or sorrow to destroy people's lives. God does not do these things and they are not any part of God's will for anybody's life. How do I know this? Because I now know what the Word says about my heavenly Father. The Word says that God is love!

John 3:16-17:

_____

_____

_____

_____

_____

_____

_____

There is no condemnation in God's love. Condemnation means to pronounce to be guilty, to sentence to punishment, or to pass judgment against, to accuse.

Revelation 12:10:

_____

_____

_____

_____

The accuser in this scripture is Satan himself. Satan charges us with offense; accuses us before our God day and night. If you are feeling condemned or being condemned by the words or actions of someone else that is the work of the enemy of your soul, Satan. That is not God speaking to you and that is not God making you feel that way. Condemnation is from the devil. It is not from God because God is love!

Romans 5:8:

_____

_____

_____

_____

God did not wait for us to be "good enough" or to believe first on Jesus before he sent his Son to die for the sins of the world. God's love is unconditional; he loves us because we are his children and he *is* love. We do not have to earn his love by doing religious works of some kind. We cannot buy his love through paying tithes and giving all we have to the poor, and we do not have to be perfect enough so we will deserve his love. While we were yet sinners, God demonstrated his love for us by sending his Son to die for our sins.

1 John 3:1:

_____

_____

_____

_____

Do we get that? We are God's children! When my three sons were born, they did not have to *do* anything for me to love them. The truth is I loved them before they were even born but oh how that love was demonstrated once they were born. I took care of my sons' every need when they could not offer me one thing in return. I gave them my undivided attention, my every waking moment, and most of my sleeping moments to nurture them, take care of them, and love them even when they could not show me in any kind of way that they loved me in return.

I John 4:16:

_____

_____

_____

_____

_____

Romans 8:37-39:

_____

_____

_____

_____

_____

_____

_____

There is nothing in this life that is stronger than God's love for us. There is no heartache, no sorrow, no hardship, and no tragedy that is more powerful than the love of God. God's love has made us victorious over every trial, every circumstance, and every temptation we will ever encounter in this earthly life. His love has already conquered and defeated the works of the devil for us!

Ephesians 2:4-5:

_____

_____

_____

_____

_____

_____

_____

God's love for us is sustainable; meaning that it never goes away or runs out. Wow! That is just amazing to me that no matter how bad we mess up and no matter how many mistakes we make God's love *never* quits! God never stops loving us! Even when we are at our lowest point in life his love is still great and immeasurable toward us!

1 Peter 5:7:

_____

_____

_____

That is love!

Isaiah 41:10:

_____

_____

_____

_____

That is love!

Lamentations 3:22-23:

_____

_____

_____

_____

That is love!

Isaiah 54:10:

_____

_____

_____

_____

_____

_____

Psalm 86:15:

_____

_____

_____

_____

Zephaniah 3:17:

_____

_____

_____

_____

So where did you read about a God of hate, a God of destruction, a God that kills people in car accidents because it is part of his plan for their life? Where did you read in the Word about a God who strikes down children with incurable diseases for some unknown reason that we will understand more about it in the sweet by and by? You will never find that in the scriptures. That is NOT the nature of God. That is NOT the nature of Jesus. That is NOT the nature of the Holy Spirit. That is not even Old Testament scripture under the Old Testament Law. If you read the Old Testament and rightly divide it and you will find that God IS, WAS, and WILL ALWAYS BE LOVE!

2 Peter 3:9:

_____

_____

_____

_____

That is love!

# Gains for Growth

1 John 4:9-10:

_____

_____

_____

_____

_____

_____

Explain in your own words what you believe this scripture means concerning the love of God.

_____

_____

_____

_____

_____

_____

John 15:9:

_____

_____

_____

_____

Jude 1:21:

_____

_____

_____

What is the connection between John 15:9 and Jude 1:21?

_____

_____

_____

_____

_____

_____

Find a scripture not already cited in this lesson that describes the steadfast love of our heavenly Father.

---

---

---

---

Scriptures for encouragement:

Psalm 136:26:

---

---

---

---

Psalm 36:7:

---

---

---

---

Deuteronomy 7:9:

_____

_____

_____

_____

You Got That From Me

# Lesson 2

## The Provider

So one evening I was reading a book and the author was describing how he spent his time in worship. He said that when he entered into worship he spent a certain amount of time just sitting still and letting God love on him. I was so startled by what I read that I laid the book down beside me and said, "You *let* God love on you?" I had never heard anything like that before. These were the next religious thoughts that went through my mind, "I thought we were supposed to love on God. I thought worship was doing something for God not having God do something for you. How can you say you *let* God love on you? That just is not right!" But then, for some reason, I started crying and I knew immediately the Lord wanted to teach me something. I picked the book back up and reread the author's statement again, "I *let* God love on me." I just could not comprehend letting God love on me because I was so conditioned to think how we are to express our love for God. For months I had been teaching, preaching, and telling of the goodness of the love of God but for some reason I was having great difficulty in accepting the idea that my heavenly Father wanted to love on me!

As I sat there crying the Lord began showing me how I love my children. He reminded me of how I would spend hours rocking my children and grandchildren; how one of my favorite things to do was to hold them, hug them, and cuddle them in my arms. He showed me how I never expected them to talk to me, hug me back, or even tell me how much they loved me. I just enjoyed holding them and having them lean into me and just be still while I loved on them. Yeah, that was a wow moment for me! The Lord continued to show me the many ways I express my love for my children and grandchildren and how my heart is always set towards doing them good. Then, the Lord said to me, "Where do you think you learned to love your children and grandchildren like that? You got that from me!"

Genesis 1:27:

_____

_____

_____

_____

Psalm 103:13:

_____

_____

_____

_____

As a mother, I always took care of my children. I made sure they had home-cooked meals, adequate clothing, toys, a home filled with love, holiday traditions, time with family, school supplies, friends, and whatever else they had need of. The Lord said, "You got that from me!"

Philippians 4:18-19:

_____

_____

_____

_____

_____

_____

_____

The word *supply* in the Greek means to cram, furnish, satisfy, finish, and to make replete; well supplied. Not only will God supply our needs but he meets every kind of need we have whether it be physical, emotional, mental, financial or spiritual. We also must understand that God is not limited by resources as we sometimes are. He meets our needs by his riches in glory. That word *riches* in the Greek means wealth, money, possessions, abundance, and a valuable bestowment. Whatever we have need of, whatever good thing that we *want*; God's got it and he wants to give it to us! How do I know this to be true?

Psalm 23:1:

_____

_____

_____

The word *want* in this scripture means that you will not be in need of anything, you will not be lacking in anything, and you will not decrease in anything!

John 10:11:

_____

_____

_____

_____

Isaiah 40:11:

_____

_____

_____

_____

Once the Lord is your Shepherd, you have amazing blessings provided for you. You see, I took extremely good care of *my* children; the children that lived in my house. Now, if my children would have run away from home or disowned me as their mother and refused to let me take care of them they never would have received all of the wonderful things that I was more than willing to do for them. But as long as they lived in my house and were a part of my family they were well taken care of. I got that from him!

Psalm 34:9:

_____

_____

_____

_____

_____

Psalm 84:11:

_____

_____

_____

_____

Let's look at how the Shepherd (Father) meets the wants and needs of his sheep (children).

Psalm 23:2:

_____

_____

_____

_____

God does not lead his children into destruction, tragedy, bankruptcy, addiction, sickness, or disease. He will bring you out of those places and lead you into green pastures where you will live in abundance! God will guide you to still, deep waters of rest and refreshing.

John 4:14:

_____

---

---

---

---

That word *thirst* in the Greek means to desire earnestly. If your life is lacking, if you know that there is something missing, if you are empty, incomplete, lonely, and have unmet needs, come to Jesus. He will meet all of your needs and fill your life with an abundance of everything!

Psalm 23:3:

---

---

---

---

The word *restore* means to repair or renovate; to put something back to its original condition. So I want you to think about this. Maybe you have been deeply hurt, abused during your childhood, betrayed by someone you loved and those situations have tarnished you. You feel robbed, cheated, dirty or unclean. Well, the love of God can restore you to your original condition. Your original condition before you were abused or hurt. Your original condition when you felt free to love and trust people. Your original condition to believe in family, friends, and love again! Our heavenly Father loves us and cares about meeting *all* of our needs. The Lord will guide us and keep us from stumbling, falling or going astray as we allow him to love on us!

Psalm 23:4:

_____

_____

_____

_____

_____

The valley of the shadow of death was in reference to the deep, waterless, gloomy, wild, beast-infested, rocky, dangerous, death-lurking ravine so common in Palestine. Does that sound anything like your life, your finances, your relationships, your job, your family, your health? Well, then there is good news for you! God loves you so much that he said he would see you safely though each and every one of these conditions. Not only will the Shepherd lead us safely through each and every circumstance but we also have no need of fearing our circumstances because of the Shepherd's constant companionship, watch, and protection.

2 Timothy 1:7:

_____

_____

_____

_____

1 John 4:18:

_____

_____

_____

_____

Fear is a spirit that is brought on by the devil. Fear is torment; it tortures your mind, your heart, and your life. Fear is paralyzing and it robs us of our faith. Our Father knows how destructive fear is and he does not want it having any rule, reign, or room in our lives. He is reassuring us through his word that no matter what we are faced with he will be with us and we need not fear any circumstance because he is our constant companion.

So not only do we have a Father who loves us so much that he walks with us through every circumstance in this life but he also comforts us by taking care of our every need as well. The comfort of the

Shepherd's rod and staff this verse is referring to is the club and crook, the only two things carried by shepherds for defense and help. The club was for the sheep's enemies and the crook for the sheep's protection. Our Shepherd's protection is better than a banny hen, momma bear, or helicopter mother!

Isaiah 26:3-4:

_____

_____

_____

_____

_____

_____

_____

Psalm 91:10:

_____

_____

_____

_____

Psalm 34:7:

_____

_____

_____

_____

Psalm 23:5:

_____

_____

_____

_____

The love of the Father brings us to a place where our enemies are powerless to affect any part of our life. We will prosper regardless of what others say about us, regardless of how others treat us, misuse us or abuse us. We will feast in safety while the Shepherd watches out for us, fights for us, and protects us. Our entire life is full to overflowing with blessedness; not only full to the brim but running over! Wow! Can you even fathom that? Every need, every want, every situation and circumstance is completely taken care of in this life by the Lord being our Shepherd because of his great love for us!

Psalm 138:7:

_____

_____

_____

_____

Matthew 5:11:

_____

_____

_____

_____

The word *blessed* in that scripture means you are happy, to be envied, supremely blessed, and well off. Whoohoo! Do you get that? Your enemies cannot stop God from blessing you. In fact, when people are your enemies because you are your Father's child you are supremely blessed. You are so happy, so peaceful, so joyful, and so well taken care of that your enemies actually envy you!

Psalm 23:6:

_____

_____

_____

_____

We can have confidence that such goodness and mercy will follow us all the days of our lives.

Psalm 34:8:

_____

_____

_____

_____

Hebrews 4:16:

_____

_____

_____

_____

Luke 1:50

_____

_____

_____

_____

You see, when the Lord is your Shepherd you have access to the love of Christ that passes all knowledge (Ephesians 3:19). Meaning, in your natural mind the love of God far exceeds what you can even imagine possible!

Ephesians 3:20:

_____

_____

_____

_____

There is no doubt that if our own children have a need; physical, financial, or even emotional we would exhaust all of our own personal, earthly resources to help our children because we love them. Right? Ok, well your heavenly Father loves you far beyond any measure of love you have for your own children. Let that sink in. Your Father loves you *more* than you love your own children! And not only is he able to do exceeding abundantly above all that we ask or think, he is *willing* to do exceeding abundantly above all that we ask or think by providing not only our needs but also our wants. Wow! That is love!

30

# Gains for Growth

Matthew 6:33:

_____

_____

_____

_____

What are the *things* Jesus is referring to in this scripture?

_____

_____

_____

Proverbs 10:22:

_____

_____

_____

_____

Explain in your own words what you believe this scripture means.

_____

_____

_____

_____

One of the seven names for God translated from the Hebrew is El Shaddai. What is the meaning of El Shaddai?

_____

_____

_____

_____

Scriptures for encouragement:

3 John 1:2:

_____

_____

_____

_____

2 Corinthians 9:8:

_____

_____

_____

_____

Psalm 37:25:

_____

_____

_____

_____

# Lesson 3

# The Comforter

I was sitting on my bed watching what seemed to be a movie reel playing in my mind while the Lord was showing me the many different ways in which I have always expressed my love for my children and grandchildren. I must say that I was quite impressed with the way I love my children and grandchildren. I mean, I really felt quite proud of myself for being such a good mom and gigi! However, it was all brought into perspective when the Lord spoke the words to my heart, "Where do you think you learned to love like that? You got that from me!" You see, I believe I love my children and grandchildren with everything that is within me. I believe I did everything within my power, ability, and available resources to take good care of my children while they were growing up and I believe I take good care of my grandchildren now. I believe I will still go to great lengths to help my children and grandchildren if they have a pressing need they are struggling with. Not to mention what I will do for them just because they *want* something. I believe I care about my children and grandchildren when they are hurting or heartbroken, when tragedy strikes, when they are sick, and when they are troubled. It is not hard for me in any kind of way to understand how much I love my children and grandchildren. So why is it so hard for us to understand that our heavenly Father's love is much greater, deeper, far reaching, and all encompassing than our love is for our very own children and grandchildren?

Psalm 103:13:

_____

_____

_____

_____

John 3:16:

_____

_____

_____

_____

God sent his Son, Jesus Christ, into this world to show us in-person the love of the Father! In the book of John we find one of the disciples, Phillip, asking Jesus to show them the Father. Jesus responds in John 14:9:

_____

_____

_____

_____

You see Jesus was the perfect will, the perfect Word, and the perfect love of the Father here on earth as a man. He walked among mankind to *show* the love of the Father to all who would believe.

Ephesians 3:16-19:

_____

_____

_____

_____

_____

_____

_____

_____

_____

_____

_____

The word *breadth* in the Greek means that God's love is boundless. It has no boundaries. It does not begin and it does not end. The word *length* in the Greek means that God's love is endless. It endures through anything and is eternal. The word *depth* in the Greek means that God's love is fathomless (unable to be measured or understood), exhaustless (unable to be emptied). The word *height* in the Greek means measureless. Are you getting the idea that God's love is so deep, so pure, so strong, and so awesome that we cannot even understand with our natural mind how extreme his love is for us.

According to the Pulpit Commentary this passage of scriptures states that the knowledge of Christ's love, in the sense of an inward personal experience of it; its freeness, its tenderness, its depth, its patience, is the great dynamic of the gospel. This love is transmuted (changed in the form, nature, or substance) into spiritual forces. As the breeze fills the sails and bears forward the ship, so the love of Christ fills the soul and moves it in the direction of God's will. Meaning; through Jesus, God's love comes to us in ways that we recognize and understand that it is God's love so that we receive his help and follow his direction. Let me explain by giving you an example of how God's love was made real to someone I know.

One of our family members in his early twenties was going through a very difficult time struggling with depression, anxiety, and just recovering from being set free from drug addiction. He was trying extremely hard to straighten out his life and make different decisions for his future but depression, loneliness, dread and fear tried to consume him constantly. On one particular day he was very upset and grieving over a friend of his who had committed suicide. He went to the graveside of this friend and sat beside his grave grieving. All of a sudden the clouds in the sky parted and the sun began to shine brighter than he had ever seen and a warm feeling enveloped him. At that very moment what seemed to be a hundred black birds took off in flight through the sky. This family member immediately recognized; knew beyond a shadow of a doubt that this was God's love and that God was showing him that he loved him and that everything was going to work out in his own life. God's love was transmuted; changed into a form of nature so that this young man would have a personal experience and know and understand that God loves him and cares about how he was feeling and what he was going through at that very moment. Now, how many times do you think this young man had seen the clouds move, the sun shine, and the birds fly? Many, many times no doubt. But on that particular day it was different because God chose to show his love through those ordinary natural means. That encounter with the love of God was a 'no turning back' point for our family member. He has continued his walk with the Lord and has experienced many great blessings spiritually, physically, and financially since that day!

So why do we find it so hard to believe that the Lord cares about what we are going through? He cares about what hurts us, what concerns us, what troubles us, *and* he does something about it!

Hebrews 4:15-16:

_____

_____

_____

_____

_____

_____

_____

_____

The word *touched* in the Greek means to have compassion; to feel sympathy. Do we get that? Jesus has compassion on us and feels sympathetic towards us when we are facing something that we are struggling with emotionally, mentally, physically, or financially. He cares about us! I have to remember this: if my children are going through a hard time, I want to help them. If my children are hurting, I want to help them. Well, I got that from him!

So, let's look at what the Word says about how much the Father and his Son, Jesus cares about what we are going through.

Matthew 9:36:

_____

_____

_____

_____

Jesus saw that the people were troubled, harassed, worried, weary and faint and it moved Jesus so strongly that he had to help them. This is a beautiful example of how deeply Jesus cares about people. He loved them so much that he was compelled to help them and meet their needs.

2 Corinthians 1:3-4:

_____

_____

_____

_____

_____

_____

_____

_____

You see our heavenly Father cares about *everything* we are going through *all* of the time. Not only does he care about what we are going through but he also wants to comfort us during all of our heartache, every trial, every hardship, every disappointment, every discouragement, and every turmoil because he is the God of comfort! There was never a time in my children's lives that I did not care about what they were going through or what they were facing. I cared, I comforted, and I offered help, loving words, sound advice, hugs, tears, and prayers: I got that from him!

Luke 7:13:

_____

_____

_____

_____

_____

The Lord cares about what we are going through when one of our loved one dies. He cares that we are weeping. He cares that we are grieving. He cares that we are scared, lonely, confused, fearful, and feeling desperate. He has compassion for us and desires to comfort us and bring us into a place of peace. He desires to heal our broken heart and to give us strength and even joy even though we have experienced a great loss to our life, our home, and our family. Yes, he cares about us that much!

John 16:33:

_____

_____

_____

_____

Jesus wants us to be happy. Jesus wants us to be at peace in all circumstances of life. Jesus wants us to be full of joy. How do I know this to be true? Because he said he overcame the world so we would have peace. Wow! What love! Jesus overcame this world for *us* so that we could have peace, joy, and happiness in this life here on earth. That is love!

Matthew 15:32:

_____

_____

_____

_____

Jesus cared so much about these people that he had to meet their needs. Whoohoo! That is amazing love. Jesus performed a miracle to meet the physical needs of people. Jesus died to pay for the sins of the world so we can have eternal life in heaven *but* Jesus is also concerned about every need we have on this earth and wants to meet our needs because he cares about us!

Matthew 11:28:

_____

_____

_____

Once again we see here in the Word how much the Lord cares about us when we are discouraged, depressed, anxious, worried, hopeless, heartbroken, scared, fearful, or upset about anything. He is not only willing to help us but he has already made provisions to do something to help us.

There has never been a time when one of my sons were hurting or having trouble in any kind of way that it did not touch me to the very core of my being. I would comfort, protect, provide, nurture, and do anything I could to rescue my children from a hurting, broken heart and I cared about everything they were going through: I got that from him! Our heavenly Father and our Savior Jesus Christ loves us far beyond what we are capable of even understanding. We have help, peace, and comfort in our time of need because God is love!

# Gains for Growth

Hebrews 4:16:

_____

_____

_____

_____

Explain in your own words what you believe this scripture means.

_____

_____

_____

_____

_____

_____

List the three most important things you would like the Lord to help you with right now. Then, find a scripture in the Bible where the Lord helped someone else in this same way or a scripture that promises help for your specific request.

For example: I need emotional healing for something that happened to me and hurt me deeply. Psalm 147:3: He heals the broken hearted, and binds up their wounds.

_____

_____

_____

_____

_____

_____

_____

_____

_____

_____

_____

Psalm 34:18-19:

_____

_____

_____

_____

_____

_____

_____

_____

Explain in your own words what these verses mean.

_____

_____

_____

_____

_____

_____

Scriptures for encouragement:

1 Peter 5:7:

_____

_____

_____

_____

Psalm 121:2:

_____

_____

_____

_____

Psalm 55:22:

_____

_____

_____

_____

# Lesson 4

## The Giver

So I want to share with you what I call *The Donuts and Chicken Story*. Let me preface the story with this little piece of information. I LOVE being a gigi which means that my grandchildren might be just a wee bit spoiled. Not much but maybe a little depending on who you ask. Ok, I cannot even write that with a straight face. You get the idea. With that being said, I am the type of gigi who always shows up with gifts. For an extended period of time it was either donuts or chicken. If I showed up in the morning I would bring donuts. If I showed up in the afternoon or evenings I would bring their favorite fried chicken and I was always greeted with hugs and screams of "Gigi's here!" Well one day I showed up on the spur of the moment. It was a rushed trip and I was running short on time so I did not have time to stop and pick up anything; no donuts and no chicken.

Well I received my usual greeting of screams, smiles, and hugs; "Gigi, you're here!" Then I hear this, "did you bring us donuts? Or did you bring us chicken?" I responded with, "Oh, I'm sorry, I didn't have enough time to make a stop before coming out." Let me tell you something, those kids were SHOCKED! "You didn't bring us anything?" Their disappointment almost made me cry. They could not believe that I would show up with nothing; no donuts, no chicken, no gifts of any kind. Why were they expecting something? Because that is all they had ever known. I had always shown up with gifts. They expect me to bring gifts. They expect me to be good to them because all I have ever been is good to them. And the Lord said, "You got that from me!"

Matthew 7:9-11:

_____

_____

_____

_____

_____

_____

_____

I know how to give good gifts to my children and grandchildren. I love giving gifts to my children and grandchildren. I love watching my children and grandchildren enjoy and have fun with the gifts I give them. It brings me pleasure to watch them enjoy the gifts I give them. I got that from him!

Romans 8:32:

_____

_____

_____

_____

Our heavenly Father is not stingy. Our heavenly Father is not waiting or longing to punish us. Our heavenly Father is not withholding any good thing from us because he wants to see us suffer in some way. Our heavenly Father wants to bless us, give us gifts, prosper us, keep us, help us, and love us!

So let's look at some of the gifts the Father has given to us. The most precious gift is the gift of Salvation; eternal life in heaven.

John 4:10:

_____

_____

_____

_____

What was the gift of God Jesus was referring to?

Romans 6:23:

_____

_____

_____

_____

Ephesians 2:8:

_____

_____

_____

_____

Another gift God brings to his children is the gift of peace.

Isaiah 26:3:

_____

_____

_____

_____

John 14:27:

_____

_____

_____

_____

Psalm 4:8:

_____

_____

_____

_____

If you have ever been heartbroken, in turmoil, fearful, anxious, panicked, depressed, distraught, or grieving, you understand how precious the gift of peace is!

How about the gift of joy!

Psalm 16:11:

_____

_____

_____

_____

John 15:11:

_____

_____

_____

Psalm 4:7:

_____

_____

_____

_____

The Lord gives us a joy that money cannot buy, things cannot give, people cannot offer and circumstances cannot take away. Joy is a gift from God!

How about the gift of wisdom, grace, the comforter, and promises of prosperity!

James 1:5:

_____

_____

_____

_____

James 4:6:

_____

_____

_____

_____

John 14:17:

_____

_____

_____

_____

2 Corinthians 9:8:

_____

_____

_____

_____

I mean that is better than donuts and chicken! God knows how to shower his children with gifts!

Psalm 103:2:

_____

_____

_____

_____

The word *benefits* in the Hebrew means his kind deeds, treatment, an act, service, requital (compensation). You see, my grandchildren receive benefits because I am their gigi. Well our heavenly Father has even greater benefits. His gifts, kind deeds, favorable treatment, and compensation for us are far greater than anything I could ever shower upon my grandchildren!

Psalm 103:3:

_____

_____

_____

_____

We have already addressed the gift of Salvation but we are also given the gift of healing. My grandchildren do not have to work for my gifts, beg for my gifts, or be deserving of my gifts. They receive my gifts because they are my grandchildren and I love them. My gifts are a benefit of them being my grandchildren. It works that same exact way with our heavenly Father. Healing is a gift, a benefit given to us because the Father loves us. You do not have to earn it, beg for it, work for it, pay for it, or be deserving of it. It is a gift. It is free. All you have to do is just receive what the Father wants to give you!

Psalm 103:4:

_____

_____

_____

_____

Psalm 5:12:

_____

_____

_____

_____

We have also been rescued from danger, destruction and death and given the gift of a new life covered by the favor and mercy of the Lord. Wow!

Psalm 103:5:

_____

_____

_____

_____

The New Living Translation states this scripture this way: He fills my life with good things! That sounds like gifts to me. Do you see how our heavenly Father wants, desires, and has planned to give us good gifts in every area imaginable? Our heavenly Father is not angry with us. He is not waiting and wanting to punish us. He is not withholding good things in order to see us suffer in some way. It is and always has been his good pleasure to bestow gifts on his children.

You see, our heavenly Father always comes bearing gifts!

Luke 12:24:

_____

_____

_____

_____

Psalm 147:11:

_____

_____

_____

_____

God loves his children. Just as it delights my soul to give gifts to my children and grandchildren, it delights our heavenly Father to give gifts to us!

# Gains for Growth

James 1:17:

_____

_____

_____

_____

Explain in your own words what you believe this scripture means.

_____

_____

_____

_____

_____

1 Corinthians 12:1:

_____

_____

_____

_____

Read 1 Corinthians 12:4-12. List 9 of the spiritual gifts given to the Body of Christ in this passage of scriptures and then describe what each gift is.

1. _____

_____

_____

_____

2. _____

_____

_____

_____

3. _____

_____

_____

_____

4. _____

_____

_____

_____

5. _____

_____

_____

_____

6. _____

_____

_____

_____

7. _____

_____

_____

_____

8. _____

_____

_____

_____

9. _____

_____

_____

_____

1 Corinthians 12:28:

_____

_____

_____

_____

What do you think some of the gifts of helps and administrations are that are given to Christians and how do you believe they are used by Christians to do a work for the Lord?

_____

_____

_____

_____

_____

_____

Scriptures for encouragement: Matthew 6:33:

_____

_____

_____

Psalm 127:3:

_____

_____

_____

Psalm 119:105:

_____

_____

_____

# Lesson 5

## The Planner

When my children were growing up I had big plans for their lives. I dreamed about everything from making their Christmas' and birthdays special to who they would marry and what they would choose for a career. I dreamed about them going to college or starting their own business or landing their dream job. I dreamed about them having a family of their own and buying their first house. Not only did I dream big for their lives but I also encouraged them to dream big for their lives. I continually praised them for being so smart, gifted, and talented. I continually praised them for every effort, every accomplishment, every hurdle, and every barrier they mastered. I prayed over them from the time they were little concerning their futures, their careers, their choices, their friendship circles, and their future wives. Why? Because it was always my hope and desire for my children to grow up happy and become successful, independent, productive men, husbands, and fathers. I wanted success for my children. I wanted happy marriages for my children. I wanted financial stability for my children. I wanted strong, healthy relationships for my children. And the Lord said, "You got that from me!"

You see our heavenly Father desires for each and every person ever born to live a happy, healthy, and prosperous life. Our heavenly Father never plans failure, defeat, loneliness, depression, addictions, or bankruptcy for any of his children's lives. Just as I dreamed big for my children, our heavenly Father dreams even bigger for us!

Jeremiah 29:11:

_____

_____

_____

_____

The NIV states this scripture this way: For I know the plans I have for you, declares the Lord, plans to prosper you and not to harm you, plans to give you hope and a future. Anyone who thinks or tells others that tragedy through car wrecks or any other kind of accident, a terminal disease, or being a victim of a violent crime or abuse, or a child being born with birth defects or a chronic illness is all part of God's plan does NOT know anything about the true nature of our wonderful, loving, heavenly Father! Do those things happen? Yes, sometimes they do. But they are NOT part of what God has planned for our lives. Those kinds of tragedies are the work of the enemy of our souls! There was not one single day that I planned, desired, or wanted in any kind of way for something bad to happen to one of my children. There was not one single day that I thought any of my children deserved or needed to be sick, hurt, or hungry. There was not one single day that I hoped when my children grew up that they would be bankrupt, homeless, or destitute. Likewise, our heavenly Father does NOT plan any of those things for our lives either!

Nahum 1:7:

_____

_____

_____

_____

So let's look at what God has planned for our lives. 3 John 1:2:

_____

_____

_____

_____

God's financial plan for your life is for you to prosper. Our heavenly Father does not want us just barely scrimping by, struggling with overdue, unmet bills. No, he wants us to prosper! The word *prosper* in the Greek means to succeed in business affairs.

Deuteronomy 8:18:

_____

_____

_____

_____

Malachi 3:10-11:

_____

_____

_____

_____

_____

_____

_____

It has never been God's plan for any of his children to live in poverty, go hungry, or go without adequate clothing or housing. God has *always* planned for *all* of his children to be blessed in all areas of our lives!

Joshua 1:8:

_____

_____

_____

_____

_____

I taught my children things that would help to make them successful like; a strong work ethic, not to steal, cheat or lie, to do unto others as you would have them do unto you, that knowledge is power, that Jesus is the way, the truth, and the life! I taught them everything they would need to know to lead and guide them into a successful life and a great future. Now, what did they have to do to live a successful life and have a great future? *Do what I taught them!* If your financial life is lacking, then go back to the Word and begin applying God's instructions to your financial decisions. God's plan for us is to prosper but it only works if we do it the way our heavenly Father designed it to work.

2 Corinthians 9:7:

_____

_____

_____

_____

Mark 10:29-30:

_____

_____

_____

_____

_____

_____

God never planned for any of his children to live in poverty. Being poor is not a sign of humility. These scriptures clearly state that whatever we give up for the sake of the gospel of Jesus Christ will be returned unto us a hundredfold *now in this time*. That means right now, on earth, in *this* lifetime and when we get to heaven. God *wants* to bless us financially! How can we, the body of Christ, spread the gospel, help the poor, take care of the widows and orphans, give away Bibles, support missionaries, and meet the needs of other people when we do not have any money to pay our own bills?

1 Timothy 6:17:

_____

_____

_____

_____

The NIV states this scripture this way: Command those who are rich in this present world not to be arrogant nor to put their hope in wealth, which is so uncertain, but to put their hope in God who richly provided us with everything for our enjoyment. It is not a sin to have money. It is not a sin to have things. It is not a sin to prosper. And not only is it not a sin, our heavenly Father actually wants us to enjoy all the things he has blessed us with. Wow! Do you get that? Just like I wanted my children to grow up and be successful our heavenly Father wants us to be successful!

Our heavenly Father also plans for us to be healthy. Sickness and disease is not God's divine will for any person's life.

1 Peter 2:24:

_____

_____

_____

_____

Why would Jesus die to pay for your sins and then it not be God's will for you to receive Salvation? Well, why would Jesus take stripes, and be wounded for you to be healed but then it not be God's will, God's plan, or God's purpose for you to be healed? It is not God's will, God's plan, or God's purpose for anyone to be sick. That is why he sent his Son to take stripes to provide healing for all sickness and disease! (We will cover this in greater depth in another lesson).

Your earthly life will succeed and prosper in direct correlation to how your soul prospers. You see, that is why so many people struggle financially, get over-looked for promotions, are in failing marriages, are in constant conflict with their family and church relationships, and are even struggling with their own happiness and contentment. Their relationship with the Lord and their Word life is lacking. They might be hearers of the Word but they are not doers of the Word.

James 1:22:

_____

_____

_____

_____

You can go to church every time the doors are open, you can sing in the choir, teach Sunday school, and cook for the church potlucks and even volunteer in the nursery. BUT, if you hate your mother-in-law, refuse to forgive someone who said or did something that hurt you, if you are not a generous, cheerful giver, if you are jealous of others, flirting with your co-workers, lying to your boss, or cheating on your taxes your soul is not prospering. Therefore, the fullness of the plans that God has for your life will not come to pass.

You see, God loves you so much and he has a good plan for your life but if you are refusing to follow his plan then obviously, *his* plan for your life will not work out. Let me explain it this way. Let's say a parent plans great things for their child and did great things to prepare those plans: taught the child right from wrong, took the child to school, helped the child with their homework, instilled morals and values and modeled them in their home, took care of the child when they were sick, taught the child how to work hard, stay out of trouble, be careful who they pick as their friends, and every other good thing a parent teachers their child so their child can grow up to be productive, successful, and happy. But the child refuses to listen to their parent and instead of doing what the parent has taught them, the child rebels and drops out of school, gets in trouble with the legal system for stealing, gambling, selling drugs, goes to jail, loses their home, their car, their marriage, their children and completely refuses to do anything right that they were taught to do. Now, did the parent plan for the child to be successful? Did the parent teach the child how to be successful? Did the parent show the child how to be successful? So why was the child not successful? Because the child did not do what the parent planned, taught, role-modeled and desired for the child to do! We must understand that our heavenly has not only planned for us to be successful but he has already made the way for us to be successful. Our heavenly Father has great plans for our life, he wants us to be prosperous, he wants us to be healthy, and he wants us to have a great relationship with him. God has made the plan. God has prepared the plan and God has taught us the plan through his Word. I choose to listen to my Father and follow the plans that he has laid out for me which are good plans; plans to prosper me and give me a hope and a future! I am going to prosper and be in health even as my soul prospers!

If your life is lacking in peace, joy, or happiness, if your finances are lacking, if your marriage is lacking, if your relationship with your parents or children are lacking, I have good news. That is not part of

God's plan for your life. It is time for a re-routing! Stop where you are. Stop what you are doing and begin to ask your heavenly Father to show you where you got off of his path and started down your own path. The minute one of my children came to me and said, "Mom, I can't do this, will you show me how?" I immediately showed my children what they needed to do to get back on track. And the Lord said, "You got that from me!"

# Gains for Growth

Luke 6:38:

_____

_____

_____

_____

Explain in your own words what you believe this scripture means.

_____

_____

_____

_____

_____

_____

Proverbs 3:9-10:

_____

_____

_____

_____

_____

_____

_____

_____

Explain in your own words what you believe these scriptures mean.

_____

_____

_____

_____

_____

What are we required to do in the above scriptures?

_____

_____

_____

_____

Matthew 6:33:

_____

_____

_____

_____

Explain in your own words what you believe this scripture means.

_____

_____

_____

_____

_____

_____

Isaiah 1:19:

_____

_____

_____

_____

Explain in your own words what you believe this scripture means.

_____

_____

_____

_____

_____

_____

Scriptures for Encouragement: Psalm 35:27:

_____

_____

_____

Psalm 128:2:

_____

_____

_____

_____

Proverbs 10:22:

_____

_____

_____

# Lesson 6

## The Forgiver

For many years in my Christian walk I lived under constant condemnation. Sad but true. Every time I made a mistake, every time I gave into a temptation, every time I failed to read my Bible enough, fast enough, pray enough, had hard feelings toward someone who offended me, said something I should not have said, or missed a church service I felt condemned and thought that God was mad at me and would not fellowship with me until I had proved in some kind way that I was worthy once again. I felt like I deserved to be punished. I thought I had to serve some kind of penance in order for my relationship to be restored to the Lord to the place where he would be pleased with me once again. I even thought when I did something wrong I could mark a prayer off my list and forget about God ever answering that one because I messed up. And because I messed up, I had to be punished and one way God punishes people is to not answer their prayers. Until one day, a glorious day, a truth day, a setting-me-free day, the day I heard a message, this message:

Romans 8:1:

_____

_____

_____

_____

I listened to a faithful servant of the Lord who has preached the gospel all over the world, seen many, many miraculous healings, and been blessed to the full promises that the Word provides explain that condemnation is a way the enemy of our soul keeps us in bondage to emotions that are not supported by the Word of God in any way. The word *condemnation* in the Greek means punishment following, penal servitude, penalty, or an adverse sentence. Wow! There was my answer! I realized how I had been living for many years in my Christian walk under condemnation. I thought I was being a good, faithful, disciplined, obedient servant all that time but the truth of the Word of God showed me how I was living under constant condemnation and that is NOT the truth the will of God concerning any born-again believer's life! Once you are born again and *in* Christ Jesus there is NO condemnation anymore; you are forgiven! Forgiven of every sin, every failure, every short-coming, every weakness, every character flaw, and every wrong thought you have ever had towards yourself, towards others, and even towards God. Totally and completely forgiven!

So let me share with you how the Lord showed me this in the natural. One of my sons came to me as an adult and began apologizing to me for everything he had put me through while he was growing up. I mean he repetitively kept saying over and over again how sorry he was for all of the trouble he caused me, for all the wrong things he had done, and for how hard he had made it on me. To which I responded, "Son, I don't remember anything you're talking about! You were a good son. I was always proud of you, and all of my memories of your childhood are good memories of fun times, your accomplishments, the things you did that were hilarious, and what a good brother you were and still are. I'm not mad at you and I don't even remember the times you got in trouble and I sure don't remember everything you got in trouble for!" And the Lord said, "You got that from me!"

You see, I do not remember what I grounded my sons for. I do not remember every time they disobeyed me. I do not remember everything they did wrong. I do not think about those things when I think of my children. When I think about my children I think about all of the amazing things they did growing up, how smart they are, all the fun we had as a family, the funny things they did to each other, and how awesome they are now! I am not mad at them for something they did when they were 10, 12, or 18 years old. I am not angry at them for disobeying me while they were growing up. Why not? Because all of that is in the past and it means NOTHING to me now! And the Lord said, "You got that from me!"

Psalm 103:10-12:

_____

_____

_____

_____

_____

_____

_____

_____

_____

God is not and does not hold our sins against us. He forgives us and then forgets about them. He does not do unto us according to our sins because he does not remember our sins! When my sons show up for Christmas dinner my thoughts towards them are not on something they did wrong from 5, 10, or 15 years ago.

Hebrews 10:17:

_____

_____

_____

_____

Hebrews 8:12:

_____

_____

_____

Isaiah 43:25:

_____

_____

_____

_____

Micah 7:18-19:

_____

_____

_____

_____

_____

_____

Go throw a penny into the depths of the sea and then go back and try to find it the next day, the next month, or the next year. You will never find that penny again; it is gone forever! Just like our sins; gone forever never to be remembered again! Whoohoo! That is why the Word tells us we are not under condemnation anymore once our sins have been forgiven. What do we have to be condemned for? Every sin that we ever committed has been cast as far as the east is from the west never to be remembered again. Now that is being free. And who the Son has set free is free indeed!

Colossians 1:13-14:

_____

_____

_____

_____

_____

_____

The word *forgiveness* in the Greek means a release, a pardon (free from the penalty or consequence). You see, the enemy of my soul wanted me to walk in condemnation and believe that I was under a constant penalty of punishment. The enemy wanted me to believe that God would refuse to fellowship with me because I was imperfect. I have a deep, divine, revelation for you; *God knows that we are all imperfect and loves us so much that he sent his Son to die for our imperfections so that we might become righteous through him!* Our imperfections do not keep God from loving us. In spite of our imperfections, God still wants a close, personal relationship with his children!

Psalm 86:5:

_____

_____

_____

_____

Acts 3:19:

_____

_____

_____

_____

The words *blotted out* in the Greek means to be wiped away, to wipe out; obliterate (utterly destroy). Wow! That does not sound like my heavenly Father is holding anything against me for my past sins!

1 John 1:9:

_____

_____

_____

_____

Guilt and shame are not emotions sent from God. God does not ignore his children because we make a mistake. God is not angry at his children for being imperfect. God does not require some type of penance in order to be in right standing with him. That was all taken care of through his Son, Jesus Christ, when he died on the Cross to pay for the sins of the world! If we were still required to do something in order to earn forgiveness then why did Jesus die for us?

Romans 4:7-8:

_____

_____

_____

_____

_____

_____

_____

Just like I do not think about anything my sons did wrong growing up. Just like I do not hold anything my sons did wrong against them. Just like I am not angry for my sons disobeying me when they were growing up, our heavenly Father does not think about our sins anymore. My sons past wrong actions never cross my mind when I think of them. My thoughts towards my children are caring, concern, fondness, praise, joy, goodness, happiness, and nothing but love! And the Lord said, "You got that from me!"

# Gains for Growth

1 John 3:20:

_____

_____

_____

_____

Explain in your own words what you believe this scripture means.

_____

_____

_____

_____

_____

Read Romans 8:33-39 and then explain in your own words what you believe these scriptures mean.

_____

_____

_____

_____

_____

_____

Matthew 26:28:

_____

_____

_____

Explain in your own words what you believe this scripture means.

_____

_____

_____

_____

_____

_____

Ephesians 4:31-32:

_____

_____

_____

_____

_____

_____

_____

_____

How are we instructed to treat people according to these scriptures?

_____

_____

_____

Find a scripture describing how God is tenderhearted towards us.

_____

_____

_____

_____

_____

Find a scripture describing how God is forgiving towards us.

_____

_____

_____

_____

Find a scripture describing how God is merciful towards us.

_____

_____

_____

_____

Scriptures for encouragement:

John 3:17:

_____

_____

_____

_____

Ephesians 1:7:

_____

_____

_____

_____

Isaiah 43:25:

_____

_____

_____

_____

# Lesson 7

## The Healer

When my children were growing up and got sick I took care of them; good care of them. There were times I stayed up all night changing bed sheets, washing out puke pans, giving medicine every four hours, and keeping cold wash cloths cold. When my children got hurt I doctored every boo-boo, kissed every bloody knee and elbow, rocked them until it quit hurting, and reassured them every single time that they would be ok. I rearranged my work schedule, my sleep schedule, my laundry schedule, and my cooking schedule to take care of my children when they were sick or hurt. I have stayed up all night taking care of child with a dog bite that required stitches in multiple wounds, a child with a broken leg, a child with a hyper-extended arm and shoulder, not to mention the tooth aches, leg aches, ear aches, eye aches, and every allergy attack, head cold, sinus infection, and stomach virus that visited.

And you know what? There was not one time that I ever thought or said, "I think I will just let them suffer this time." Never once did I go about being their parent and refuse, neglect, or forsake taking care of my children. I never once told them, "You brought this on yourself so you are just going to have to live with it." I never once left them in their room without medicine, without comfort, or without care. I never told them I was trying to teach them a lesson, punish them for something, or just did not care about how they felt or what they were going through. I never once *made* my child sick, *wanted* my child to get sick or stay sick, and I never left my child to just *be* sick without doing anything to take care of them. My day, my life, my routine, my schedule, nor my heart returned to normal until my child was well again. And the Lord said, "You got that from me!"

Ephesians 5:1-2:

_____

_____

_____

_____

_____

_____

_____

The word *followers* in the King James Version was translated from the Greek word *imitators*. An imitator is a person who copies the behavior or actions of another. The idea that God puts sickness on his children to teach them a lesson, punish them, show them something, or to draw them closer to him is unscriptural. God is the creator, not the destroyer. God is love. Now, does sickness and disease exist? Yes. Does sickness and disease attack Christians? Yes. Does sickness and disease attack children? Yes. But God does not *make* people sick. God does not *let* people get sick and God does not *want* people to stay sick. (For a more complete teaching on where sickness and disease came from and how to get rid of it please read my Bible study *Hello Healing: Goodbye Sickness & Disease)*.

Just as I took care of my children when they were sick, our heavenly Father has made provisions for us to be taken care of when we are sick.

Proverbs 4:22:

_____

_____

_____

_____

_____

_____

The word *health* in the King James Version was translated from the Greek meaning *medicine, cure, deliverance.* Wow! How amazing is that? The Word of God is actually medicine to our bodies! Just like I gave my children medicine when they were sick or hurt our heavenly Father gave us medicine for when we are sick or hurt. Yes that is what that means. The Word of God is medicine for your body!

Psalm 107:20:

_____

_____

_____

_____

So we have the written Word of God that is medicine but God did not stop there.

Isaiah 53:4-5:

_____

_____

_____

_____

_____

The word *griefs* and *sorrows* in the King James Version translated from the Hebrew mean *disease* and *pain.* Jesus carried; took on, all diseases and pain that would ever afflict our bodies. He did not just die for our sins but he also bore all sickness and disease on the Cross of Calvary!

1 Peter 2:24:

_____

_____

_____

_____

John 1:1:

_____

_____

_____

_____

This verse is talking about Jesus.

John 14:11:

_____

_____

---

---

This verse is talking about Jesus. You see, just like I never left my kids in their bed sick, hurting, weak and unable to take care of their selves without any help of any kind just to suffer our heavenly Father does not leave us sick, hurting, weak, and unable to take care of ourselves without any help of any kind just to suffer either. He gave us medicine for our flesh, for our bodies, he sent his Word. If you need healing in your body you need to get into the Word of God and take it just like natural prescription medicine; three times a day!

There were times when my children were sick or hurt that I could take care of them myself with over the counter medicine and a band-aid. But there were also some times when my children were sick or hurt that I took them to the doctor because I needed help that was beyond what I could do for them. And the Lord said, "You got that from me!" Let me explain what I mean. God provided that same help for us when we need something more than what we can do for ourselves.

James 5:14-15:

---

---

---

_____

_____

_____

_____

_____

1 Corinthians 12:9-10:

_____

_____

_____

_____

_____

_____

_____

Our heavenly Father still gives the gifts of healing and the working of miracles to those who choose to believe in them. The days of miracles and healings are not over. There are many people still today that are divinely healed of incurable diseases because the supernatural medicine of the Word healed, cured, and delivered!

Jeremiah 30:17:

_____

_____

_____

_____

Our heavenly Father has supplied every provision we need in order for us to be healed and for us to recover from injuries. God has taken care of us in every way possible. He does not want us to be sick. He does not make us sick. He does not want us to suffer with sickness. It hurt my heart to see my children sick. I would, and did do everything in my power as a mom to take care of them and help them. And the Lord said, "You got that from me!"

Psalm 147:3:

_____

_____

_____

_____

My heavenly Father does not want any of his children to suffer with sickness or disease. He loves us so much that he provided medicine and help for us in our time of need. He does not forsake us or neglect us when we are sick. He loves us and wants us well just like I wanted my children well when they were sick!

# Gains for Growth

Proverbs 17:22:

_____

_____

_____

_____

Explain in your own words what you believe this scripture means.

_____

_____

_____

_____

_____

_____

_____

Proverbs 16:24:

_____

_____

_____

_____

Explain in your own words what you believe this scripture means.

_____

_____

_____

_____

_____

_____

Acts 10:38:

_____

_____

_____

_____

Matthew 9:35:

_____

_____

_____

_____

Matthew 12:13:

_____

_____

_____

_____

Hebrews 13:8:

_____

_____

_____

_____

Explain in your own words what you believe this scripture means.

_____

_____

_____

_____

_____

_____

_____

Scriptures for encouragement: Psalm 41:3:

_____

_____

_____

_____

Psalm 103:3:

_____

_____

_____

_____

2 Corinthians 1:3:

_____

_____

_____

_____

_____

# Lesson 8

## The Teacher

I believe one of the most natural things a parent does for their children is to teach them. It begins with teaching them language. I mean who does not remember screaming the first time their child said momma or da-da? Then, it continues with teaching them how to feed their self, dress their self, pick up after their self and the list goes on. As my children began to get a little older my teaching shifted from teaching them how to do things to teaching them lessons such as; do not touch a hot stove or you will get burned, do not run with scissors, hold my hand in a parking lot and do not run out in front of cars, no, you cannot use a knife to cut up your own steak because you are only five! I taught my children lessons about how to be safe because I did not want them to get hurt or injured.

As they continued to grow up the lessons began to include things such as; always tell the truth; honesty is the best policy. Along with, why choosing the right friends is important; birds of a feather flock together. How choosing to go to the right places is important; there is safety in numbers. Choosing to do the right thing is important because there is guilt by association. I taught my children these lessons because I did not want them to get into trouble and suffer the terrible consequences of bad decisions. I taught my children because I wanted them to have a great childhood, get a good education at school, respect their teachers, elders, and law enforcement, have good friends they could have good fun with, and grow up into a hard-working, productive member of society all the while being a great husband and father. I taught my children because I wanted them to be able to live a happy, successful life that would be full of goodness and joy not death, depression, misery, and terrible consequences that could destroy their future. And the Lord said, "You got that from me!"

Matthew 5:1-2:

_____

_____

_____

_____

_____

_____

_____

_____

Notice that Jesus taught them by saying; by speaking words.

The next nine verses Jesus teaches the beatitudes. The next four verses Jesus teaches about being the salt and the light. The next four verses Jesus teaches about the law. The next six verses Jesus teaches about anger. The next four verses Jesus teaches about lust. The next two verses Jesus teaches about divorce. The next five verses Jesus teaches about making vows. The next five verses Jesus teaches about retaliation. The next six verses Jesus teaches about loving your enemies. The next four verses Jesus teaches about giving to the needy. The next 11 verses Jesus teaches about prayer. The next three verses Jesus teaches about fasting. The next six verses Jesus teaches about money. The next 10 verses Jesus teaches about worry. The next six verses Jesus teaches about criticizing others. The next six verses Jesus teaches about asking and receiving. The next two verses Jesus teaches about heaven. The next six verses Jesus teaches about bearing fruit; being productive. The next seven verses Jesus teaches about being wise.

Not one time in these scriptures do you find where Jesus made anyone sick to teach them a lesson. Not one time in these scriptures do you find where Jesus caused a car wreck, train wreck, motorcycle wreck or any other accident in order to teach anyone a lesson. Not one time in these scriptures do you read where Jesus taught anyone a lesson through a violent crime, abuse, or any other form of tragedy. No, Jesus taught by saying, by words, by the same way I taught my children. I never pushed my children out in front of a car to teach them that running in a parking lot could be dangerous. I never cut my children with a knife to teach them that a knife is sharp and they should not play or run with it. I never gave my children poison to drink to teach them to obey me. No, I used words to teach my children just like the Lord uses words to teach us. There is an answer and a teaching for every topic, every circumstance, and every question you will ever have in this lifetime in the Bible. God is not a mystery. Life is not a mystery. Death is not a mystery, and eternity is not a mystery. There was never a time in my children's lives that they came to me with a question and I refused to answer or withheld an answer from them. Our heavenly Father *wants* us to learn of the goodness of his Kingdom, the goodness of his love, and the goodness of his plans for us!

So let's look at just a few of the teachings of the Father in addition to what Matthew records. Remember how I said that I taught my children about things that could hurt them, injure them or that were dangerous? Well I got that from him! Our heavenly Father teaches us about everything that is harmful to us or dangerous to our life or our future in any kind of way. Pride is one of the most destructive forces any person can fall prey to. It will not only destroy you but it will destroy your relationships, your finances, your character, reputation, and testimony, until it eventually destroys your mind and heart.

Proverbs 16:18:

_____

_____

_____

Proverbs 11:2:

_____

_____

_____

Proverbs 29:23:

_____

_____

_____

James 4:6:

_____

_____

_____

_____

_____

Proverbs 16:5:

_____

_____

_____

_____

Galatians 6:3:

_____

_____

_____

_____

Proverbs 26:12:

_____

_____

_____

_____

The scriptures clearly teach us that pride is extremely destructive to our lives.

Now, let's look at what the Word says concerning the danger and destruction that is caused by lying.

Proverbs 12:22:

_____

_____

_____

_____

Proverbs 19:9:

_____

_____

_____

_____

You see, not only does lying cause our heavenly Father to be displeased with us but lying also brings negative, unfruitful consequences into our very own lives, relationships, and circumstances. We do *ourselves* harm when we engage in lying!

Luke 8:17:

_____

_____

_____

_____

I remember telling my children when they were growing up that I would find out the truth whether they told it to me or not. Well, I got that from him! This is a universal law concerning the promises of the Word of God that applies to every human being whether they are saved or not. Truth prevails every time and lies told in secret will always be exposed to the light!

Proverbs 26:27:

_____

_____

_____

_____

Our heavenly Father is teaching us that if we lie about other people, about situations, about what we have said or done to try to manipulate and deceive other people for our own benefit or out of bitterness and hatred we are the one who will be destroyed by the

118

very lies we told about others. I will put this scripture in my own words: if you set out to destroy someone, you will; you will destroy yourself!

Finally, let's look at what the Word says about the destruction and danger of sin.

Romans 6:23:

_____

_____

_____

_____

Remember, Jesus came to pay for the wages of sin so we do not have to! God never intended for us to be bound by sin, destroyed by sin, or die in our sin. Our loving Savior came so that we can be free from the wages of sin! Whoohoo!

John 8:34:

_____

_____

_____

_____

Jesus is teaching us that sin is bondage, slavery, a heavy yoke and burden and there is no freedom in sin. There is only freedom in Jesus! Sin is not going to give us a good future, a promising hope, or bring blessings into our lives. Sin only brings destruction, shame, regret, depression, misery, and death! What is exciting about all of that? I mean, I can tell you from personal experience that I was never happy when my life was destroyed, my finances were destroyed, and my reputation was destroyed because of the sinful lifestyle I was living. But when I was no longer a slave to sin; when I became free to live in peace, joy, blessings, goodness, and mercy oh my goodness did happiness ever flood my life! I was free from the wages of sin. I was free the heavy yoke and burden of bondage. I was free to live!

I am thankful for a loving Father who continually teaches me through his Word how to be successful, happy, prosperous, and healthy. I am thankful for a loving Father who leads me in every circumstance and situation in this life by his Word so that I can learn to make the right decisions that will benefit my life and the lives of every person I am able to impact for the Kingdom of God. I am thankful for a loving Father who does not withhold instruction from me but is willing to teach me through his Word everything and anything that I am willing to learn! I am honored and absolutely love it when my children come to me with a question because they want to know what mom thinks they should do. And the Lord said, "You got that from me!"

# Gains for Growth

Find at least one scripture that teaches about the following topics:

Forgiving others:

_____

_____

_____

_____

How to treat your neighbor:

_____

_____

_____

_____

Paying tithes & giving offerings:

_____

_____

_____

_____

How a husband should treat his wife:

_____

_____

_____

_____

How a wife should treat her husband:

_____

_____

_____

_____

What you should do if someone says or does something to offend you:

_____

_____

_____

_____

One way to be a good steward with your money:

_____

_____

_____

_____

What to do if you are not sure about making a decision:

_____

_____

_____

_____

How to increase your faith:

_____

_____

_____

_____

The power of the words you speak:

_____

_____

_____

_____

Scriptures for encouragement:

Proverbs 22:6:

_____

_____

_____

_____

1 Peter 4:10:

_____

_____

_____

_____

Psalm 32:8:

_____

_____

_____

_____

# Lesson 9

## The Seer

As a mother, I have always seen my children differently than most people who know them, meet them, taught them, coached them, hired them, befriended them, and even loved or hated them. A teacher might have seen my children as, uh let's say; too cool for school. I just saw them as being "all boys". A coach might have seen my children as lacking focus or determination. I saw them trying as hard as they could. An employer might have seen my children as unmotivated or uninterested. I saw them working hard and giving it their best shot. The world might see my children as nobody's. But I see my children as the apple of my eye, the beat of my heart, and the reason I can call myself a mom and gigi. My children can light up my day in a way that no other person in this world can. To me, they are instant happiness and an ever present loving joy!

My children grew up being told they could be whatever they wanted to be if they worked hard enough. My children grew up being told how smart, talented, and gifted they were. My children grew up being told, "You can do it, you got what it takes, and you're smart enough, strong enough, and talented enough to do it!" You see, I saw something in my children that they did not always see in their selves. I saw potential in them. I saw ability in them. I saw talent in them. There were times when my children said, "Mom, I can't do it" and I said, "Yes you can, I know you can do it because I know who you are!" And the Lord said, "You got that from me!"

Our heavenly Father knows who we are. He knows what our talents and abilities are and what we can do even when we do not!

1 John 3:1:

_____

_____

_____

_____

Galatians 3:26:

_____

_____

_____

_____

2 Corinthians 6:18:

_____

_____

_____

_____

And just as I saw my children differently than other people did, our heavenly Father sees us differently than the world does!

2 Corinthians 5:17:

_____

_____

_____

_____

The world might see you as the trouble-maker, the liar, the thief, the gossip, the addict, or the sinner that you once were but your heavenly Father sees you as a new creature. To him, you are not who you once were! Our Father does not see us based on our past sins, our past actions, or our past lifestyle. Everything about us is new in the eyes of the Father!

Ephesians 2:10:

_____

_____

_____

_____

Our heavenly Father sees us as a worthy, new creature as if we had never committed one single sin! Wow! Let that sink in!

2 Corinthians 5:21:

_____

_____

_____

_____

Righteousness means that we are in right standing with God. Therefore, we can stand in the presence of God as though we had never done wrong. We can stand in God's presence without a sense of condemnation or a spiritual inferiority complex. Other people may see our mistakes, our past sins, or our wrong doings, but that is not how our heavenly Father sees us! If someone came to me and tried to tell me all about every single thing my child did wrong when they were in the 3$^{rd}$ grade, 8$^{th}$ grade, or a senior in high school I would say, "That was a lifetime ago. My son has graduated, started a career, is raising a family, running his own business, serving his country; he's not a 3$^{rd}$ grader anymore!" I see my children successful now and I am not interested in their past mistakes; they are in the past. And the Lord said, "You got that from me!"

Romans 8:37:

_____

_____

_____

_____

You are not a nobody, who cannot do anything, who has no purpose, no gifts, no talents, who is so unworthy, so undeserving, so down-trodden, who messes everything up. No! That is not how your heavenly Father sees you. He sees you as a conqueror. He sees you as well able to be successful. You are more than deserving of a good job, a good family, a loving home, a promotion, a successful business, and a good education. You are able to overcome every obstacle, every barrier, every hater, every deceiver, and every abuser. You are not held captive to any of these things any longer! And not because I say so. I am not just giving you a pep talk. I am telling you what your heavenly Father thinks and says about you!

Philippians 4:13:

_____

_____

_____

_____

What can you not do? Why can you not succeed? What can you not become? What do you not deserve? Why are you not worthy? Your heavenly Father just said that you cannot be conquered. You cannot be defeated and you CAN do all things through Christ Jesus!

Deuteronomy 8:18:

_____

_____

_____

_____

Your heavenly Father sees you prosperous, wealthy, and living in abundance whether you do or not. Not only does he see you that way, he has also made a way for you to live in abundance. It is not God's desire for his children to live in poverty, to go without, to have unmet needs or live in lack in any area of our lives!

Psalm 128:2:

_____

_____

_____

_____

Psalm 1:3:

_____

_____

_____

_____

Psalm 37:25:

_____

_____

_____

_____

I am telling you that your Father wants you to be successful. He wants you to be prosperous and he wants you to live in abundance in every aspect of your life.

Colossians 1:13-14:

_____

_____

_____

_____

_____

_____

_____

Your heavenly Father sees you as forgiven and redeemed. You are free from the penalty of sin. You are free from the death of sin. God does not see you as a slave to Satan. God does not see you in bondage. God does not see you as a captive or as a prisoner to sin any longer!

Romans 6:18:

_____

_____

_____

_____

John 8:36:

_____

_____

_____

_____

Psalm 32:1:

_____

_____

_____

_____

Your heavenly Father sees you as blessed whether you see yourself that way or not.

Psalm 146:5:

_____

_____

_____

_____

Psalm 32:1:

_____

_____

_____

_____

Ephesians 1:3:

_____

_____

_____

_____

Even when we think we are at our lowest point in this life, even when we face heartbreak or betrayal from others our Father says we are blessed!

Matthew 5:4:

_____

_____

_____

_____

Matthew 5:10-11:

_____

_____

_____

_____

_____

_____

_____

You see, just as I have always seen my children differently than most people who know them, meet them, taught them, coached them, hired them, befriended them, and even loved them our heavenly Father sees us much differently than the world does, than our friends and family do, and he even see us differently than we see ourselves sometimes. I saw potential in my children that they never saw in themselves. I had confidence in my children's abilities that they never felt in themselves, and I knew beyond a shadow of a doubt that my children could succeed when they did not think there was even a fighting chance. And the Lord said, "You got that from me!"

# Gains for Growth

1 Samuel 16:7:

_____

_____

_____

_____

In your own words, explain what this scripture means to you.

_____

_____

_____

_____

Jeremiah 29:11:

_____

_____

_____

_____

Based on this scripture do you believe God wants ALL his children to be successful? Why or Why not?

_____

_____

_____

_____

Psalm 139:13-14:

_____

_____

_____

_____

_____

_____

Explain in your own words what these scriptures mean to you.

_____

_____

_____

_____

_____

Matthew 5:14:

_____

_____

_____

_____

Explain in your own words what this scripture means to you.

_____

_____

_____

_____

_____

_____

Describe any 'aha' moments or revelation you have received concerning a greater understanding of how your heavenly Father sees you.

_____

_____

_____

_____

_____

_____

Scriptures for encouragement: Psalm 138:8:

_____

_____

_____

_____

John 15:15:

_____

_____

_____

_____

1 John 4:4:

_____

_____

_____

_____

# Lesson 10

## The Accommodator

I am the mom of three boys. So, I made my mind up a long time ago that when the time came, I would be the best mother-in-law a daughter-in-law could ever have! I made a conscious decision that I would treat my daughter-in-laws like queens. I would *not* be a meddling, nosy, opinionated, mother (in-law) who had to be all up in my adult children's business, marriage, financial decisions, or child-rearing. Believe it or not, I *want* my daughter-in-laws to like me, love me, and want to be around me. I also want to be someone they can turn to when they need something. So I have made it my practice that when my children are facing a problem or a difficult circumstance I always ask them, "what do you want me to do?" And then that is what I do. I do not assign myself a role, or barge in and do what I feel like doing. I try to be sensitive to what they want or need me to do. I mean, I prided myself on accommodating my sons and my daughter-in-laws during their times of need so you can just imagine how humbling it was when the Lord said, "You got that from me!"

In Matthew 20:30-31 we find that two blind men were sitting by the roadside and when they heard that Jesus was passing by, they cried, "Lord, have mercy on us, Son of David!" But the crowd rebuked them, telling them to be quiet but they cried out again even louder. Now notice how Jesus responded in verses 32-34:

_____

_____

_____

_____

_____

_____

_____

_____

_____

_____

What do you want me to do for you? Wow! Did you get that? Jesus asked what he could for them. I mean for years I thought my entire Christian life was based on what I could do for Jesus; not what he could do for me!

We find another example of a man asking Jesus to do something for him in Matthew 8:2-3:

_____

_____

_____

_____

_____

_____

I mean do you see how easy that was? The man came to Jesus and asked Jesus to do something for him; to heal him. And Jesus immediately responded, "I will, be thou clean!" You see, sometimes I think we get it in our head, mind, and heart that we have to beg Jesus for umpteen years to do something for us. Yet, that is not what the Scriptures record. Jesus never told anyone they would have to wait or come back tomorrow. Jesus never told anyone that he would think about it and let them know what he decided. Jesus *always* responded to the immediate needs of the people who came to him with, "I WILL!"

Hebrews 13:8:

_____

_____

_____

The centurion came to Jesus saying that his servant is lying paralyzed at home, suffering terribly and this is Jesus' response in Matthew 8:7:

_____

_____

_____

_____

Jesus not only said, "I will" to healing but he also said, "I will" in Matthew 11:28:

_____

_____

The word *labor* in the Greek means to grow weary, tired, exhausted with toil or burdens or grief. The words *heavy laden* in the Greek means to be loaded with a burden of unwarranted precepts or rules that are used to control or influence us. One example of this could be in reference to strict regulations enforced at work, through the government, or even by our community or local businesses which causes strife and divisions among coworkers, neighbors, or even family and church members. The word *rest* in the Greek means to cause or permit you to cease from any movement or labor in order to recover and collect your strength, to refresh, to keep quiet and be calm.

Jesus *will* give you peace! If you are stressed in your body and mind, if you are anxious in your heart, if your thoughts and fears seem to be consuming your every waking and sleeping moment, Jesus has promised that he *will* give you rest! Jesus will do for you what no vacation, no time-off from work, no shopping trip, hunting trip, or road trip can do. Jesus will take your burden, your load you are carrying, your pressures and he will cause you to cease from working, thinking, worrying, toiling, and fearing and instead give you strength to refresh and remain calm. Wow! How accommodating is that? How awesome is that? How caring is that?

Notes:

_____

_____

You see, our loving Savior really does care about what we are going through, how we feel when the pressures of life seem to be consuming us, and not only does he care, but he wants to help us in our times of need. So not only will he give us rest but he will also give us power to overcome whatever this life holds!

Matthew 16:19:

_____

_____

_____

_____

The delivery of the keys to a city or kingdom symbolizes the handing over of the authority to the person the keys are given to. According to Pulpit Commentary, the Kingdom of Heaven in this verse references the visible Church of Jesus Christ in its most extended form. Jesus was literally handing over his power and authority to his church. The word *bind* in the Greek mean to fasten, throw into chains, or declare to be prohibited; banned, not allowed. So when you are binding something you are declaring that it is not allowed in your life, in your family, in your finances, in your physical body or in your mind or your emotions. The word *loose* in the Greek means to undo anything bound, tied, or compacted together, to dismiss, break up, to deprive of authority, whether by precept or act, to demolish, destroy, or dissolve something into parts, to overthrow, or do away with. Do you get that? Jesus gave us the power to overthrow whatever the devil is throwing at us! Jesus gave us the power to destroy and dissolve the fiery darts of the devil. Satan has no authority over you, over your health, over your finances, over your emotions, or over your spirit in the name of Jesus when you bind and loose on earth what is trying to affect or impact your life in a negative, destructive manner. When you bind and loose on earth according to the authority Jesus has given you all of heaven is in agreement with you. The forces of heaven will back up what you have bound and loosed. Whoohoo! What a generous display of the Father's love! Our heavenly Father does not leave us at the mercy of the devil. He made provisions for us to be victorious no matter what might happen here on this earth. This provision is also promised by Jesus in Luke 10:19:

_____

_____

_____

_____

We are not left powerless, comfortless, helpless, or hopeless! We have been given power and authority over all the power of the enemy. We have been given mighty spiritual weapons that are greater than the enemy's fiery darts. Our Father loves us and just as I would go to great lengths to protect my children, God has gone to great lengths to protect his children!

Finally, let's look at the greatest accommodation Jesus ever made.

John 6:37:

_____

_____

_____

_____

Jesus made an accommodation for my sins, for your sins, for all sins. There is no sin too great for Jesus to forgive!

1 Timothy 1:13:

_____

_____

_____

_____

Throughout the Word of God we find examples of extreme forgiveness extended to murderers, adulterers, whoremongers, thieves, liars, prostitutes, drunkards, and offenders of violent crimes of all kinds. Our wonderful Savior extends love, grace, and forgiveness no matter how many times you have sinned, no matter how many times you have failed, no matter how many times you have tried and given up. He will still in no wise cast you out when you come to him! Why? Because of Numbers 23:19:

_____

_____

_____

_____

And Hebrews 13:8:

_____

_____

_____

Just like Jesus went about meeting the needs of all people while he walked this earth, it is still his desire to meet our needs now. The provisions are the same and the promises are for us.

Our heavenly Father loves us with a love greater and more pure than any love we have ever known. He cares about what we are going through, what breaks our heart, what concerns us, what pressures we are facing, what conflict we are trying to overcome, what disappointments have shattered our dreams, and what sickness and diseases have attacked our bodies. Our heavenly Father desires to help his children, provide for his children, and comfort and protect his children. He showers loving-kindness, favor, and goodness on all of his children. I encourage you today; let the Father love you like you have never been loved before!

# Gains for Growth

Find another scripture other than Matthew 11:28 that promises us rest when we grow weary.

_____

_____

_____

_____

Describe a situation you have gone through (or are going through) that has caused you to grow weary.

_____

_____

_____

_____

_____

Now describe the moment you received rest concerning that situation.

_____

_____

_____

_____

_____

_____

List three things you would like to bind and loose on earth. (Example: My finances)

_____

_____

_____

_____

Now write a statement of declaration over each of these three things according to what we previously covered in this lesson concerning the meaning of binding and loosing. (Example: I overthrow, destroy and demolish the impact Satan has been having on my finances through the economy, my job, and my stuff breaking down. I loose the blessings of God on my finances in Jesus name!)

_____

_____

_____

_____

_____

_____

_____

_____

Scriptures for encouragement: Psalm 86:15:

_____

_____

_____

Romans 5:8:

_____

_____

_____

_____

Romans 8:32:

_____

_____

_____

_____

Milton Keynes UK
Ingram Content Group UK Ltd.
UKHW020634080923
428296UK00013B/762